# SCHONELL'S ESSENTIAL
# SPELLING LIST
## Workbook 2

**FRED J SCHONELL**

| | | | |
|---|---|---|---|
| laugh | lately ✓ | motor | lonely ✓ |
| laughed | safely ✓ | visitor | likely |
| laughter | nicely ✓ | victory | likeness |
| linger | lovely | inform | weakness |

☆ Learn the words, then use them to do the exercises.

☆ **WORD PUZZLE**   Use words from the list to complete the puzzle.

**Clues down**

2  pleasantly
3  express mirth
5  a failing
6  automobile
7  recently

8  expression
   of mirth
9  triumph
10  probable
11  not dangerously

**Clues across**

1  delay departure
4  similarity
7  expressed mirth
8  beautiful

12  to tell
13  without
    companions
14  caller

☆ **WORD HUNT**   Which words in the list have these smaller words inside them?

1  one _____

2  ice _____

3  for _____

4  ate _____

☆ **WORD MAKER**   Use words from the list to complete the words below.

1  _ _ _ _ ly (solitary)

2  late ly (possible) ✓

3  love ly (beautiful) ✓

4  _ _ _ _ ly (recently)

| servant | though | arrive | constant |
| merchant | through | advice | admit |
| distant | empire | adventure | amuse |
| important | admire | nature | ashamed |

☆ Learn the words, then use them to do the exercises.

☆ **OPPOSITES**   Find words in the list which mean the opposite of these words.

1  near _____

2  trivial _____

3  fickle _____

4  despise _____

5  depart _____

6  proud _____

7  deny _____

☆ **WORD PUZZLE**   Use the word 'important' to help form nine words from the list.

| | |
|---|---|
| 1 _ _ _ i _ _ | counsel |
| 2 _ m _ _ _ | entertain |
| 3 _ _ p _ _ _ | many territories under one ruler |
| 4 _ o _ _ _ | despite the fact that |
| 5 _ _ r _ _ _ _ | going in at one side and out at the other |
| 6 _ t _ _ _ | a wild, primitive state |
| 7 _ _ a _ _ | a buyer and seller of goods |
| 8 _ n _ _ _ _ | a risky undertaking |
| 9 _ _ t _ _ _ | one paid to do household duties |

☆ **WORD HUNT**   Complete these sentences with words from the list.

1  The word with the same letters as 'taverns' is _____.

2  The word with the most vowels is _____.

3  The word with only two consonants is _____.

4  Something which is far away is _____.

5  When you do something wrong you feel _____.

6  An _____ is an exciting event.

7  When something doesn't change, it is _____.

| | | | |
|---|---|---|---|
| evening | object | sailor | rough |
| event | subject | tailor | tough |
| equator | robin | railway | rainy |
| enough | holiday | daily | rocky |

☆ Learn the words, then use them to do the exercises.

☆ **WORD HUNT**   Fill the gaps in the poem with words from the list.

### Jones and Chaney

Captain Jones, a former (1) _____,

And Thomas Chaney, village (2) _____,

Decided they would go away

And book themselves a (3) _____.

Their (4) _____ was to find a crater

On a mountain high on the (5) _____.

The seas were (6) _____, the weather (7) _____.

The second (8) _____ Jones said, "Chaney,

Conditions here are pretty (9) _____.

Believe me, friend, I've had (10) _____.

Why don't we go to the (11) _____ station

And find another destination?"

"I quite agree," Tom Chaney said.

They went to Canada instead

And found a place where many fountains

Poured headlong down the (12) _____ Mountains.

They went out fishing three times (13) _____

And caught big salmon, fresh and scaly.

Each night occurred the same (14) _____.

A (15) _____ sang just by their tent.

Until they gave him from their dish

His nightly piece of tasty fish.

Now Canada is in their blood.

They won't come home. They're there for good!

| | | | |
|---|---|---|---|
| **sparrow** | **village** | **ought** | **thought** |
| **swallow** | **cabbage** | **bought** | **ragged** |
| **valley** | **carrot** | **brought** | **scatter** |
| **valleys** | **gallop** | **fought** | **brass** |

☆ Learn the words, then use them to do the exercises.

☆ **WORD HUNT**   Which words in the list have these smaller words inside them?

1  car  _____

2  ill  _____

3  row  _____

4  cat  _____

5  cab  _____

6  wall  _____

7  alleys  _____

8  rag  _____

9  thou  _____

☆ **WORD PUZZLE**   Use the word 'brought' to help make seven words from the list.

|   |   |
|---|---|
| b | purchased |
| r | metal made from copper and zinc |
| o | fast ride on a horse |
| u | struggled against |
| g | small country community |
| h | believed |
| t | express duty or obligation |

☆ **EXPLANATIONS**   Complete these sentences with words from the list.

1  The word which means 'conveyed' is _____.

2  Another word for 'spread' is _____.

3  Another word for 'struggled' or 'quarrelled' is _____.

4  A _____ is a low stretch of land between hills.

☆ **WORD HUNT**   Complete these sentences with words from the list.

1  There was a _____ tear in the curtain.

2  I polished the _____ candlestick.

3  The horse took off at a _____.

| alone | nasty | vanish | fancy |
|-------|-------|--------|-------|
| across | hasty | banish | ugly |
| among | shady | perish | polish |
| against | study | parish | Welsh |

☆ Learn the words, then use them to do the exercises.

☆ **WORD PUZZLE**   Use words from the list to complete the puzzle.

**Clues down**

1 opposed to
2 hurried
4 unpleasant
5 area served by a church
6 ornamented
9 expel
11 of unpleasant appearance

**Clues across**

1 from one side to the other
3 solitary
7 in the midst of
8 full of shade
10 look at closely
12 disappear
13 belonging to Wales
14 to make shiny

☆ **WORD MATCH**   Find words in the list which mean the same as these words.

1 disappear _____   4 quick _____

2 exile _____   5 horrible _____

3 die _____   6 amidst _____

☆ **OPPOSITES**   Find words in the list which mean the opposite of these words.

1 slow _____   3 appear _____

2 for _____   4 plain _____

| lawn | lays | beauty | faithfully |
| dawn | laying | beautiful | welcome |
| famous | laid | careful | until |
| dangerous | thankful | carefully | unable |

☆ Learn the words, then use them to do the exercises.

☆ **WORD HUNT**   Which words in the list have these smaller words inside them?

1  am  _____

2  come  _____

3  law  _____

4  anger  _____

5  it  _____

6  aid  _____

☆ **WORD PUZZLE**   Use the word 'unable' to help form six words from the list.

| 1 u |  |  |  |  |  |  | not possible to do |
| 2 n |  |  |  | | | | up to |
| 3 a |  |  | | | | | puts down |
| 4 b |  |  |  | | | | loveliness |
| 5 l | o | v | e | n | e | s s | putting down |
| 6 e |  |  |  | | | | gladly receive |

☆ **OPPOSITES**   Find words in the list which mean the opposite of these words.

1  sunset  _____

2  ugly  _____

3  ungrateful  _____

4  careless  _____

5  carelessly  _____

6  safe  _____

☆ **WORD MATCH**   Find words in the list which mean the same as these words.

1  lovely  _____

2  renowned  _____

3  loyally  _____

| | | | |
|---|---|---|---|
| glance | protect | stumble | scramble |
| advance | monster | grumble | bundle |
| distance | bough | thimble | kindle |
| France | plough | tremble | noble |

☆ Learn the words, then use them to do the exercises.

☆ **WORD MAKER**   Use words from the list to complete the words below.

1 _ _ _ le        (showing high character or qualities)

2 _ _ _ _ le       (to light)

3 _ _ _ _ _ le      (to complain)

4 _ _ _ _ _ le      (to shake)

☆ **WORD HUNT**   Which words in the list have these smaller words inside them?

1  rot _____

2  on _____

3  lance _____

4  him _____

5  bun _____

6  ramble _____

7  kind _____

8  tumble _____

9  van _____

10  ran _____

11  rumble _____

12  tan _____

☆ **WORD PUZZLE**   Use words from the list to complete the puzzle.

**Clues down**

1  trip

2  a hasty look

3  go forward

4  shake

6  cap for finger when sewing

8  main branch of a tree

**Clues across**

5  inhuman person

7  land of the French

9  dignified

10  agricultural implement

| | | | |
|---|---|---|---|
| tight | bucket | error | Scottish |
| slight | trumpet | terror | mutton |
| delight | shrub | ribbon | blossom |
| mighty | liberty | cotton | correct |

☆ Learn the words, then use them to do the exercises.

☆ **WORD PUZZLE**   Use words from the list to complete the puzzle.

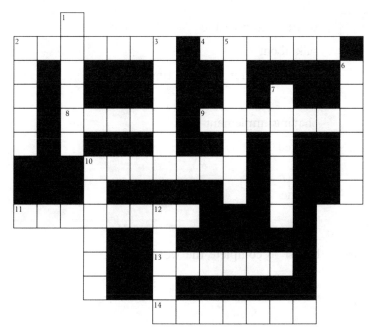

**Clues down**

1  pail
2  closed firmly
3  great fear
5  freedom
6  flesh of sheep
7  strong
10  fibre used to make cloth
12  woody bush

**Clues across**

2  brass musical instrument
4  trivial
8  mistake
9  great pleasure
10  right
11  belonging to Scotland
13  narrow strip of material
14  bloom

☆ **OPPOSITES**   Find words in the list which mean the opposite of these words.

1  slack _____

2  weak _____

3  wrong _____

4  slavery _____

5  serious _____

☆ **WORD MATCH**   Find words in the list which mean the same as these words.

1  pleasure _____

2  freedom _____

3  fear _____

4  mistake _____

| chalk | gaze | discover | size |
|-------|------|----------|------|
| stalk | blaze | distinct | prize |
| salt | razor | discuss | dislike |
| alter | lazy | distress | disgrace |

☆ Learn the words, then use them to do the exercises.

☆ **WORD PUZZLE**   Use the word 'distress' to help make eight words from the list.

| | | |
|---|---|---|
| 1 d | | to find disagreeable |
| 2 i | | talk about |
| 3 s | | learn about for the first time |
| 4 t | | stem |
| 5 r | | shaving implement |
| 6 e | | a fixed look |
| 7 s | | clear |
| 8 s | | shame |

☆ **WORD MAKER**   Use words from the list to complete the words below.

1  _ al _   (used to flavour food)

2  _ _ al _   (soft, white limestone)

3  al _ _ _   (to change)

4  _ _ _ ze   (bright flame)

5  _ _ _ ze   (a reward for success)

6  _ _ ze   (dimension)

☆ **OPPOSITES**   Find words in the list which mean the opposite of these words.

1  energetic   _____

2  lose   _____

3  well-being   _____

4  hazy   _____

| nation | company | rubber | question |
| station | companion | bullet | appear |
| dictation | astonish | quarrel | quart |
| motion | publish | barrel | quarter |

☆ Learn the words, then use them to do the exercises.

☆ **WORD PUZZLE**    Use words from the list to complete the puzzle.

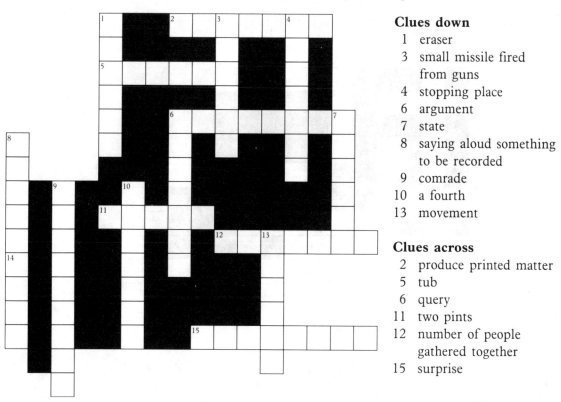

**Clues down**
1  eraser
3  small missile fired
   from guns
4  stopping place
6  argument
7  state
8  saying aloud something
   to be recorded
9  comrade
10  a fourth
13  movement

**Clues across**
2  produce printed matter
5  tub
6  query
11  two pints
12  number of people
    gathered together
15  surprise

☆ **WORD HUNT**    Complete these sentences with words from the list.

1  The word of which 'pea' is a part is _____.

2  The word of which 'ton' is a part is _____.

3  The word of which 'let' is a part is _____.

| | | | |
|---|---|---|---|
| **horrid** | **belief** | **wharf** | **occupy** |
| **coffee** | **believe** | **wharves** | **hollow** |
| **occur** | **grieve** | **niece** | **forgotten** |
| **occurred** | **ourselves** | **piece** | **combine** |

☆ Learn the words, then use them to do the exercises.

☆ **WORD HUNT**   Which words in the list have these smaller words inside them?

1  cup  _____

2  low  _____

3  bin  _____

4  off  _____

5  pie  _____

6  elves  _____

☆ **WORD PUZZLE**   Use words from the list to complete the puzzle.

**Clues down**
2  happened
3  dock
5  plural of 3 down
6  to live in
7  daughter of your sister
8  feel great sorrow
12  opinion

**Clues across**
1  not solid
4  unpleasant
6  happen
9  plural of 'myself'
10  bit
11  join together
13  accept as true
14  not remembered

| | | | |
|---|---|---|---|
| **caught** | **stir** | **knit** | **office** |
| **taught** | **stirred** | **knitting** | **officer** |
| **daughter** | **mirror** | **knight** | **different** |
| **naughty** | **bonnet** | **skill** | **skirt** |

☆ Learn the words, then use them to do the exercises.

☆ **WORD HUNT**   Fill in the gaps in the story with words from the list.

Mrs Smith is a woman police (1) _____. When she is not busy in the

(2) _____ she loves to (3) _____. She makes lots of

(4) _____ clothes. Last month she made a (5) _____ and a

(6) _____ to match. She put them on and looked at herself in the

(7) _____. She was very pleased with her (8) _____.

☆ **WORD MAKER**   Use words from the list to complete the words below.

1   _ augh _        (trapped)

2   _ augh _        (gave instruction to)

3   _ augh _ _ _    (girl child)

4   _ augh _ _      (badly behaved)

5   _ _ ir          (move around)

6   _ _ ir _        (female clothing)

7   _ ir _ _ _      (looking glass)

☆ **WORD HUNT**   Which words in the list have these smaller words inside them?

1   net      _____

2   red      _____

3   ill      _____

4   rent     _____

5   night    _____

| | | | |
|---|---|---|---|
| potato | value | instead | foe |
| potatoes | continue | steadily | poetry |
| tomato | statue | weary | butcher |
| tomatoes | thread | wearily | shilling |

☆ Learn the words, then use them to do the exercises.

☆ **WORD PUZZLE** Use words from the list to complete the puzzle.

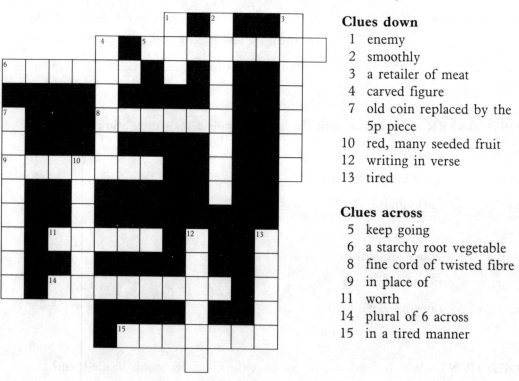

**Clues down**

1 enemy
2 smoothly
3 a retailer of meat
4 carved figure
7 old coin replaced by the 5p piece
10 red, many seeded fruit
12 writing in verse
13 tired

**Clues across**

5 keep going
6 a starchy root vegetable
8 fine cord of twisted fibre
9 in place of
11 worth
14 plural of 6 across
15 in a tired manner

☆ **WORD HUNT** Complete these sentences with words from the list.

1 My brother made a lovely salad with lettuce and red _____.

2 The _____ of Liberty is in the USA.

3 Give me a needle and _____ and I'll darn it.

| tunnel | pleasant | groan | defeat |
| suppose | pleasure | coach | tiger |
| cunning | measure | toast | reward |
| muddy | treasure | throat | shoe |

☆ Learn the words, then use them to do the exercises.

☆ **WORD HUNT**   Fill in the story with words from the list.

### A Clever Prince

A (1) _____ had grown too old to hunt but he had not lost his

(2) _____. He let it be known that there was a great (3) _____

hidden in the (4) _____ where he had his den. The entrance was very

(5) _____. Many treasure seekers got stuck in the mud and were eaten by the

beast.

The king decided to offer a (6) _____ to the one who killed the beast.

His own son said, "I (7) _____ a prince should show an example. It will give

me great (8) _____ to slay this beast."

The prince pretended to be stuck in the mud. Seeing this, the animal thought, "What a

(9) _____ surprise! Another easy dinner for me." He opened his jaws to seize

the prince. But the prince, who had taken off a (10) _____, rammed it down

the creature's (11) _____. The animal gave a loud (12) _____

and choked to death.

The king had watched the creature's (13) _____ from the royal

(14) _____. Pouring out a (15) _____ of wine he said, "Let us

drink a (16) _____ to my brave son. From now on he shall rule in my place."

And so he did, and wisely too, for many a long day.

☆ **WORD MATCH**   Find words in the list which mean the same as these words.

1  sly     _____     3  beat  _____

2  delight _____     4  nice  _____

| | | | |
|---|---|---|---|
| obey | dwelling | group | prettier |
| obeyed | wedding | wound | prettiest |
| swept | herring | youth | beginning |
| crept | vessel | calm | journey |

☆ Learn the words, then use them to do the exercises.

☆ **WORD HUNT** Which words in the list have these smaller words inside them?

1 tie _____

2 din _____

3 ring _____

4 urn _____

5 well _____

6 beg _____

7 wept _____

8 be _____

9 up _____

10 you _____

☆ **WORD PUZZLE** Use the word 'beginning' to help form nine words from the list.

|   |   | b |   |   |   | carry out orders |
|---|---|---|---|---|---|---|
|   |   | e |   |   |   | ship or container |
|   |   | g |   |   |   | small band |
|   |   | i |   |   |   | more pretty |
|   |   | n |   |   |   | place of residence |
|   |   | n |   |   |   | marriage ceremony |
|   |   | i |   |   |   | most pretty of all |
|   |   | n |   |   |   | trip or voyage |
|   |   | g |   |   |   | fish with large silvery scales |

☆ **WORD HUNT** Complete these sentences with words from the list.

1 The _____ was deep but the doctor said it didn't need stitches.

2 We decided to swim because the sea was so _____.

3 The cat _____ up on the mouse and pounced on it.

| | | | |
|---|---|---|---|
| recall | demand | feather | health |
| result | deliver | leather | healthy |
| beyond | depend | weather | wealthy |
| shiver | delay | breath | meant |

☆ Learn the words, then use them to do the exercises.

☆ **STEP WORDS**   Use words from the list to complete the puzzle.

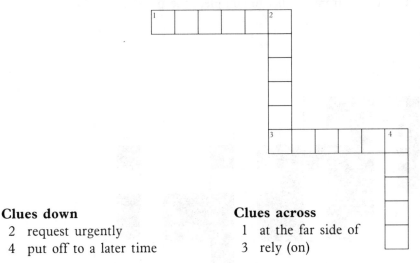

**Clues down**

2  request urgently
4  put off to a later time

**Clues across**

1  at the far side of
3  rely (on)

☆ **WORD MAKER**   Use words from the list to complete the words below.

1  _ _ ea _ _     (air drawn in by the lungs)

2  _ ea _ _ _ _   (skin of animals)

3  _ ea _ _ _ _   (degree of warmth or coldness)

4  _ ea _ _ _ _   (growth on body of bird)

5  _ ea _ _ _ _   (sound in body)

6  _ ea _ _ _ _   (rich)

☆ **EXPLANATIONS**   Complete these sentences with words from the list.

1  Another word for 'remember' is _____.

2  Another word for 'tremble' is _____.

3  Another word for 'consequence' is _____.

4  'Physical state' means _____.

5  Another word for 'intended' is _____.

| | | | |
|---|---|---|---|
| fleet | drown | aim | deer |
| screen | drowned | claim | steer |
| greedy | powder | praise | queer |
| freedom | petrol | dairy | engage |

☆ Learn the words, then use them to do the exercises.

☆ **WORD PUZZLE** Use words from the list to complete the puzzle.

**Clues down**

1 odd
2 guide
4 gluttonous
5 dust or tiny loose particles
7 a frame to conceal something
8 killed by immersion in liquid
9 intention
10 fuel for motor engines

**Clues across**

3 employ
6 commend
8 animals with antlers
11 liberty
12 store room for milk and cream
13 kill by immersion in water
14 quick
15 a demand for payment

☆ **WORD MATCH** Find words in the list which mean the same as these words.

1 shelter _____

2 peculiar _____

3 liberty _____

4 employ _____

5 avaricious _____

6 direct towards _____

| | | | |
|---|---|---|---|
| guilty | season | medal | Briton |
| guide | reason | metal | British |
| guest | crimson | mental | Irish |
| warn | iron | board | Ireland |

☆ Learn the words, then use them to do the exercises.

☆ **WORD PUZZLE**    Use the word 'Ireland' to help form seven words from the list.

belonging to Britain

belonging to Ireland

a period of the year

responsible for an offence

cause

deep red

long thin piece of sawn timber

☆ **WORD HUNT**    Which words in the list have these smaller words inside them?

1   ton   _____

2   war   _____

3   and   _____

4   rim   _____

5   met   _____

6   oar   _____

7   men   _____

8   on   _____

☆ **WORD MAKER**    Use words from the list to complete the words below.

1   _ _ _ al          (metal disc often given as award)

2   _ _ _ _ _ al       (of the mind)

3   gu _ _ _        (one who shows the way)

4   gu _ _ _        (person who gets hospitality)

5   _ _ _ _ on       (Autumn is one)

6   _ _ _ _ _ on     (a colour)

7   _ _ on          (a kind of metal)

| relate | desire | bathe | December |
| retire | deserve | vase | October |
| restore | behave | rare | Germany |
| refuse | bravery | square | herd |

☆ Learn the words, then use them to do the exercises.

☆ **WORD PUZZLE** Use words from the list to complete the puzzle.

**Clues down**
1  be worthy of
2  uncommon
3  bring back to health
4  vessel for holding flowers
7  rubbish
9  give up work for good
10  tenth month of the year
13  conduct oneself

**Clues across**
1  long for
3  tell
5  open area in a town
6  land of the Germans
8  courage
11  large group of cattle
12  twelfth month of the year
14  swim for pleasure

☆ **WORD HUNT** Complete these sentences with words from the list.

1  She was awarded a medal for _____.

2  There was a _____ of cattle in the field.

3  My parents are going to _____ to Spain.

| attend | edge | flour | lodge |
| attack | hedge | sour | bridge |
| wreck | badge | trout | sword |
| wrong | judge | stout | check |

☆ Learn the words, then use them to do the exercises.

☆ **WORD PUZZLE**    Use words from the list to complete the puzzle.

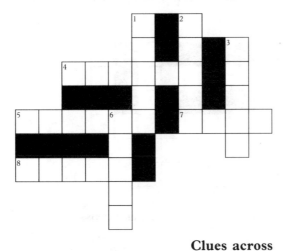

**Clues down**

1  destroy
2  a boundary or shrubs
3  decide upon a case
6  examine

**Clues across**

4  be present at
5  launch an assault
7  margin
8  emblem

☆ **OPPOSITES**    Find words in the list which mean the opposite of these words.

1  right  _____

2  defend  _____

3  slim  _____

4  sweet  _____

☆ **WORD HUNT**    Complete these sentences with words from the list.

1  The _____ over the river was unsafe.

2  I caught a large _____ in the river and cooked it for dinner.

3  My sister forgot to put the _____ in the cake.

4  The _____ in the grounds of the big house was up for sale.

5  The _____ fight in the film was very exciting.

| | | | |
|---|---|---|---|
| suit | member | wore | bowl |
| fruit | remember | score | factory |
| orange | remembered | whom | basement |
| banana | memory | weather | pavement |

☆ Learn the words, then use them to do the exercises.

☆ **MINI PUZZLE**   Use words from the list to complete the puzzle.

**Clues down**
1  a yellow fruit
2  word used at times instead of 'who'
3  twenty
4  ability of the brain to remember

**Clues across**
1  round, open container
5  a citrus fruit
6  deteriorated from constant use
7  building where goods are manufactured

☆ **WORD MAKER**   Use words from the list to complete the words below.

1  _ _ _ _ ment   (sidewalk)

2  _ _ _ _ ment   (cellar)

3  _ ui _   (set of garments)

4  _ _ ui _   (edible part of a plant)

☆ **WORD HUNT**   Complete these sentences with words from the list.

1  The word _____ is part of two other words in the list.

2  Another word for 'recall' is _____.

3  Another word for 'climate' is _____.

4  The word which contains 'e' four times is _____.

| | | | |
|---|---|---|---|
| using | eight | figure | pour |
| during | weight | scripture | court |
| duty | weigh | creature | shoulder |
| truth | dumb | entertain | huge |

☆ Learn the words, then use them to do the exercises.

☆ **WORD PUZZLE**    Use words from the list to complete the puzzle.

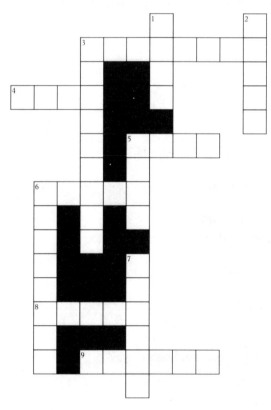

**Clues down**

1  very big
2  a proven fact
3  a sacred book
5  a task that one feels bound to perform
6  a living being
7  human form

**Clues across**

3  where the arm joins the body
4  cause to flow in a stream
5  unable to speak
6  a king's household
8  making use of
9  for the duration of

☆ **WORD HUNT**    Complete these sentences with words from the list.

1  The child has been deaf and _____ since birth.

2  Four and four make _____.

3  The boxer had to _____ in before the fight.

4  We had some drinks _____ the interval.

5  The box was a terrible _____ and I couldn't lift it.

6  The clowns will _____ the children next Tuesday.

| | | | |
|---|---|---|---|
| **exchange** | **reply** | **worship** | **city** |
| **except** | **drying** | **worse** | **cities** |
| **excuse** | **carrying** | **worst** | **circle** |
| **piano** | **foggy** | **worry** | **palace** |

☆ Learn the words, then use them to do the exercises.

☆ **WORD HUNT**   Which words in the list have these smaller words inside them?

1  an   _____

2  hang   _____

3  dry   _____

4  car   _____

5  ties   _____

6  use   _____

7  ace   _____

8  ship   _____

☆ **WORD PUZZLE**   Use words from the list to complete the puzzle.

**Clues down**
1  answer
2  apart from
5  large towns

**Clues across**
2  swap
3  pardon
4  a royal residence
6  ring
7  in a more unpleasant way

☆ **WORD HUNT**   Complete these sentences with words from the list.

1  It's the _____ weather we've had for years. It was very

_____ last night and there were twelve accidents in the

_____ centre.

2  My brother is always in trouble. He's a great _____ to my parents.

| | | | |
|---|---|---|---|
| giant | coin | earnest | seldom |
| engine | noisy | search | quite |
| divide | sign | French | wicked |
| mistake | signal | honest | selfish |

☆ Learn the words, then use them to do the exercises.

☆ **OPPOSITES**   Find words in the list which mean the opposite of these words.

1  quiet  _____

2  untrustworthy  _____

3  often  _____

4  multiply  _____

5  dwarf  _____

6  good  _____

7  insincere  _____

☆ **WORD PUZZLE**   Use words from the list to complete the puzzle.

**Clues down**
1  belonging to France
2  error

**Clues across**
3  machine
4  having no thought for others

☆ **EXPLANATIONS**   Complete these sentences with words from the list.

1  To provide a signature is to _____ your name.

2  To 'look for' means the same as to _____.

3  A _____ is a piece of metal money.

4  A _____ is an action or message used to send a warning.

5  _____ can mean 'completely'.

| | | | |
|---|---|---|---|
| throne | area | local | cruel |
| choke | idea | several | Tuesday |
| clothes | family | second | Wednesday |
| owe | people | fortune | disgust |

☆ Learn the words, then use them to do the exercises.

☆ **WORD HUNT**   Fill in the gaps with words from the list.

The (1) _____ (2) _____ always wear their best

(3) _____ on (4) _____ when they meet their friends at the

market.

☆ **WORD PUZZLE**   Use the word 'Wednesday' to help form nine words from the list.

be in dept

stop the breathing of

plan

large sum of money

region or district

loathing

a sixtieth of a minute

group of husband, wife and children

third day of the week

☆ **WORD HUNT**   Which words in the list have these smaller words inside them?

1  on  _____

2  eve  _____

3  rue  _____

4  are  _____

5  gust  _____

6  am  _____

☆ **WORD HUNT**   Complete these sentences with words from the list.

1  He won a _____ on the pools.

2  There is a large _____ of wasteland near my home.

3  I met _____ of my friends at the party.

4  The king sat on his _____.

| picnic | aunt | pencil | holy |
|--------|------|--------|------|
| arithmetic | saucer | ocean | pony |
| flood | farewell | collar | navy |
| wooden | else | clumsy | losing |

☆ Learn the words, then use them to do the exercises.

☆ **WORD PUZZLE**   Use words from the list to complete the puzzle.

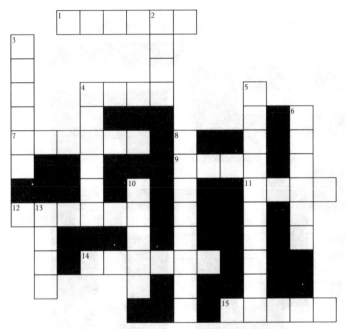

**Clues down**

2  a nation's warships
3  awkward
4  meal eaten outside on a trip
5  calculating numbers
6  part of a garment worn round the neck
8  goodbye
10  great outpouring
13  in addition

**Clues across**

1  suffering loss
4  a small horse
7  small round dish
9  sister of a parent
11  sacred
12  a writing tool
14  made of wood
15  very large stretch of sea

☆ **WORD HUNT**   Complete these sentences with words from the list.

1  The opposite of 'winning' is _____.

2  The opposite of 'hello' is _____.

3  The word with the same letters as 'tuna' is _____.

4  The word with the same letters as 'canoe' is _____.

| | | | |
|---|---|---|---|
| address | regret | lawyer | apply |
| afford | regard | gardener | allow |
| assist | retreat | passenger | allowed |
| approach | respect | drawer | clown |
| account | nerve | chapter | refer |

☆ Learn the words, then use them to do the exercises.

☆ **WORD PUZZLE**   Use words from the list to complete the puzzle.

**Clues down**

2  a solicitor is one
3  make mention of
6  have enough money to buy something
7  report or explanation
8  help
10  courage
11  put in a request

**Clues across**

1  permitted
3  admiration
4  one who draws
5  part of a book
8  come nearer
9  comic entertainer
11  let
12  place where you live
13  feeling of loss

☆ **WORD MAKER**   Use words from the list to complete the words below.

1  re _ _ _ _ _ _   (to admire)
2  re _ _ _ _ _ _   (to go back)
3  re _ _ _ _   (to be sorry about)

4  _ _ _ _ _ er   (one who practises the law)
5  _ _ _ _ _ _ _ er (one who tends gardens)
6  _ _ _ _ _ _ er   (part of a book)

| | | | |
|---|---|---|---|
| direct | ankle | confess | vote |
| detect | sparkle | confine | devote |
| destroy | humble | confuse | vast |
| destroyed | feeble | consider | plaster |
| describe | steeple | convict | pastime |

☆ Learn the words, then use them to do the exercises.

☆ **WORD PUZZLE**   Use words from the list to complete the puzzle.

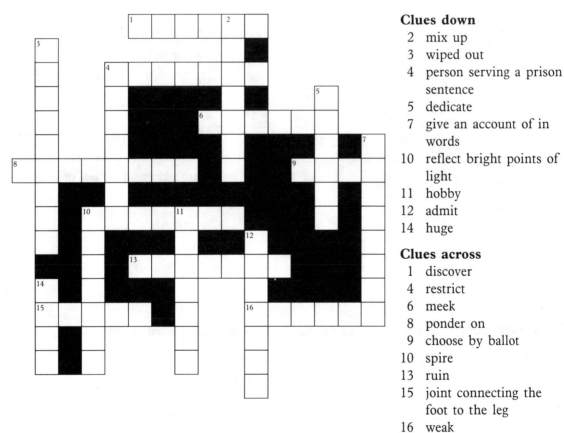

**Clues down**

2   mix up
3   wiped out
4   person serving a prison sentence
5   dedicate
7   give an account of in words
10   reflect bright points of light
11   hobby
12   admit
14   huge

**Clues across**

1   discover
4   restrict
6   meek
8   ponder on
9   choose by ballot
10   spire
13   ruin
15   joint connecting the foot to the leg
16   weak

☆ **WORD HUNT**   Complete these sentences with words from the list.

1   My father is building a new house. I helped him _____ the walls this week.

2   The policewoman helped _____ the traffic during the rush hour.

| | | | |
|---|---|---|---|
| inhabit | educate | pupil | stupid |
| insist | education | peril | insect |
| invent | information | profit | sole |
| industry | position | credit | dose |
| increase | composition | splendid | whose |

☆ Learn the words, then use them to do the exercises.

☆ **WORD PUZZLE**   Use the word 'information' to help make eleven words from the list.

| Puzzle | Clue |
|---|---|
| 1 ___ i ___ ___ ___ | express a strong belief |
| 2 ___ n ___ ___ ___ ___ | create or devise |
| 3 ___ f ___ ___ | gain |
| 4 ___ o ___ | medicine to be taken |
| 5 ___ r ___ ___ ___ ___ | get bigger |
| 6 ___ m ___ ___ ___ ___ ___ ___ | essay |
| 7 ___ a ___ ___ ___ | teaching given at school or college |
| 8 ___ t ___ ___ | hard work |
| 9 ___ i ___ ___ | slow witted |
| 10 ___ o ___ ___ ___ ___ | situation |
| 11 ___ n ___ ___ ___ ___ | live in |

☆ **WORD HUNT**   Which words in the list have these smaller words inside them?

1  hose _____      5  edit _____

2  mat _____       6  lend _____

3  pup _____       7  sect _____

4  ate _____       8  so _____

☆ **WORD MATCH**   Find words in the list which mean the same as these words.

1  danger _____      3  gain _____

2  marvellous _____      4  foolish _____

| | | | |
|---|---|---|---|
| future | dismiss | final | failure |
| pasture | display | finally | total |
| furniture | dismay | gradual | equal |
| manufacture | disorder | gradually | equally |
| departure | disappear | usually | really |

☆ Learn the words, then use them to do the exercises.

☆ **OPPOSITES**   Find words in the list which mean the opposite of these words.

1  success  _____

2  past      _____

3  arrival   _____

4  joy        _____

5  appear   _____

6  hurried   _____

7  rapidly   _____

8  tidiness  _____

9  hide       _____

10  engage  _____

☆ **EXPLANATIONS**   Fill the gaps in the poem with words from the list.

To (1) _____ is to make by machine or hand.

Where sheep and cattle graze is (2) _____ land.

The (3) _____ whistle ends the football game.

When things are (4) _____ they are all the same.

Much (5) _____ consists of beds and chairs.

Dividing (6) _____ gives equal shares.

(7) _____ and discharge (8) _____ mean the same.

For (9) _____, sum is just another name.

When things are said to (10) _____ unfold

They (11) _____ take some time, I'm told.

And when things happen (12) _____, it's plain,

You'll never find them happening again.

☆ **WORD HUNT**   Which words in the list have these smaller words inside them?

1  miss  _____.

2  fact  _____.

3  order  _____.

4  play  _____.

| | | | |
|---|---|---|---|
| Africa | breeze | wonderful | China |
| America | freeze | respectful | Arctic |
| Canada | squeeze | awful | frozen |
| Atlantic | sleeve | yawn | degree |
| Pacific | agreeable | fully | gem |

☆ Learn the words, then use them to do the exercises.

☆ **WORD PUZZLE** Use words from the list to complete the puzzle.

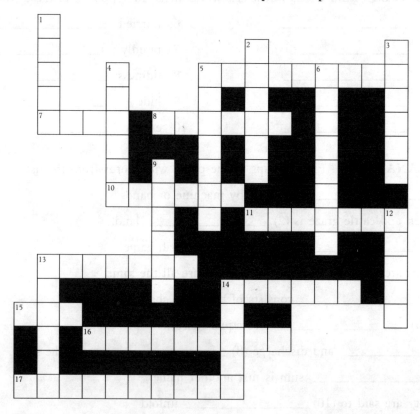

**Clues down**
1 entirely
2 turned into ice
3 university award
4 country north of USA
5 the USA
6 The world's second largest ocean
9 become very cold

12 world's most populous country
13 part of garment covering the arm
14 nasty

**Clues across**
5 pleasant
7 open the mouth wide and take in air when sleepy

8 light wind
10 second largest continent
11 world's largest ocean
13 press firmly
14 ocean surrounding the North Pole
15 jewel
16 marvellous
17 showing esteem or regard

| hero | pickle | climate | chorus |
|------|--------|---------|--------|
| heroes | knuckle | private | single |
| negro | trample | cultivate | jungle |
| negroes | title | decorate | article |
| echo | entitle | decoration | measles |

☆ Learn the words, then use them to do the exercises.

☆ **WORD PUZZLE**   Use the word 'decoration' to help form ten words from the list.

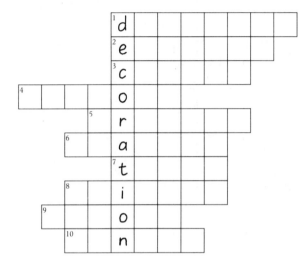

make more attractive

allow

group of singers

plural of negro

not widely known

disease common to children

name

weather conditions

plural of 'hero'

dense forest

☆ **MINI PUZZLE**   Use words from the list to complete the puzzle.

**Clues down**
  1  a reflected sound
  2  vegetables preserved in vinegar
  4  black person

**Clues across**
  3  grow
  5  finger joint
  6  not married
  7  very brave person

☆ **WORD HUNT**   Which words in the list have these smaller words inside them?

1  ample _____    3  art  _____

2  ration _____    4  mate  _____

| Europe | mere | fraction | telephone |
|---|---|---|---|
| Asia | merely | direction | switch |
| India | sincere | condition | sketch |
| Australia | sincerely | reduction | lantern |
| Russia | severe | protection | fear |

☆ Learn the words, then use them to do the exercises.

☆ **WORD PUZZLE**   Use words from the list to complete the puzzle.

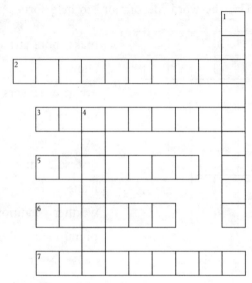

**Clues down**
1  genuinely
4  light with a
   transparent case

**Clues across**
2  defence
3  device which transmits
   and receives speech
5  genuine
6  a rapid drawing
7  state of health

☆ **WORD HUNT**   Fill in the gaps with words from the list.

(1) _____ is the smallest continent and largest island in the world.

(2) _____, the next smallest continent, is only a (3) _____ of

the size of (4) _____, the largest.

☆ **WORD HUNT**   Which words from the list have these smaller words inside them?

1  red _____

2  eve _____

3  rely _____

4  witch _____

5  direct _____

| | | | |
|---|---|---|---|
| terrible | saddle | northern | limb |
| horrible | struggle | southern | modern |
| possible | puzzle | eastern | modest |
| impossible | latter | western | screw |
| improve | parrot | shepherd | nephew |

☆ Learn the words, then use them to do the exercises.

☆ **WORD HUNT**   Fill in the gaps with words from the list.

### The Opposite Parrot

There was once an old (1) _____ whose only relative was his young

(2) _____. They had little money so it was a (3) _____ to make

ends meet. One day the boy caught a (4) _____. "I will teach it to speak,"

the boy said. But whatever the boy said, the bird always said the opposite.

"Say northern," the boy said.

"(5) _____," said the bird.

"Say possible," the boy said.

"(6) _____," said the bird.

"Say eastern," the boy said.

"(7) _____," said the bird.

"Say ancient," said the boy.

"(8) _____," said the bird.

"Say boastful," said the boy.

"(9) _____," said the bird.

The boy said, "This is (10) _____. You will have to

(11) _____, you (12) _____ bird. It must be

(13) _____ for you to learn." But the bird never did.

It has been a (14) _____ to the boy ever since.

☆ **WORD HUNT**   Complete these sentences with words from the list.

1  The word _____ has a silent 'b'.

2  The opposite of 'southern' is _____.

3  The word _____ has 'sad' inside it.

| | | | |
|---|---|---|---|
| **double** | **dispute** | **regular** | **flourish** |
| **trouble** | **displease** | **popular** | **prey** |
| **couple** | **disobey** | **particular** | **victim** |
| **courage** | **district** | **singular** | **cigar** |
| **encourage** | **disturb** | **vinegar** | **calendar** |

☆ Learn the words, then use them to do the exercises.

☆ **WORD PUZZLE**   Use the word 'particular' to help form ten words from the list.

| | |
|---|---|
| p | quarrel |
| a | bravery |
| r | move with sweeping strokes |
| t | one who is tricked or swindled |
| i | refuse to carry out orders |
| c | region |
| u | remarkable |
| l | pair |
| a | offend |
| r | disarrange |

☆ **WORD HUNT**   Complete these sentences with words from the list.

1  Your _____ is a person who closely resembles you.

2  _____ attenders at school are rarely absent.

3  Angling is a _____ pastime in Britain.

4  When you _____ people you give them lots of help.

5  An eagle is a bird of _____.

6  He causes _____ wherever he goes.

☆ **WORD MAKER**   Use words from the list to complete the words below.

1  _ _ _ _ _ _ar        (someone who is liked is this)

2  _ _ _ _ _ _ _ar       (a list of days, weeks and months)

3  _ _ _ _ _ _ar        (usual or customary)

4  _ _ _ _ _ _ _ _ _ar  (special)

5  _ _ _ _ _ _ar        (a sour liquid)

| | | | |
|---|---|---|---|
| erect | canal | mistress | trial |
| elect | capital | misfortune | loyal |
| election | rural | mischief | royal |
| electric | mortal | handkerchief | rascal |
| halt | funeral | handsome | musical |

☆ Learn the words, then use them to do the exercises.

☆ **WORD PUZZLE**   Use words from the list to complete the puzzle.

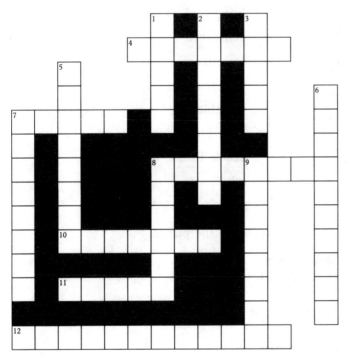

**Clues down**

1  in the country
2  woman in charge
3  manmade waterway
5  powered by electricity
6  bad luck
7  choice by vote
8  deadly
9  good looking

**Clues across**

4  talented in music
7  choose by voting
8  naughtiness
10  chief city of a country
11  befitting a king or queen
12  small square of material for wiping the nose

☆ **WORD HUNT**   Complete these sentences with words from the list.

1  I had to _____ at the traffic lights.

2  The _____ in court took four days.

3  Two hundred mourners attended the _____.

4  The house took nine months to _____.

5  He is a _____ supporter of that football team.

6  The little _____ is always in mischief.

| | | | |
|---|---|---|---|
| detain | procure | revive | secret |
| retain | endure | revenge | select |
| complain | feature | reverse | request |
| bargain | torture | resolve | require |
| waist | secure | resemble | inquire |

☆ Learn the words, then use them to do the exercises.

☆ **WORD PUZZLE**   Use the word 'resemble' to help form eight words from the list.

bring back to life

vengeance

look like

kept from others

grumble

something bought cheaply

decide firmly

ask

☆ **MINI PUZZLE**   Use words from the list to complete the puzzle.

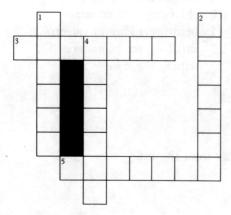

**Clues down**
1 hold back
2 need
4 cause great pain

**Clues across**
3 main film at a cinema
5 obtain

☆ **WORD HUNT**   Which words in the list have these smaller words inside them?

1 quest _____    4 is _____

2 elect _____    5 verse _____

3 end _____

| | | | |
|---|---|---|---|
| ordinary | image | exact | exist |
| library | imagine | exactly | example |
| January | imagination | expand | bury |
| February | examine | extract | buried |
| enemy | examination | exercise | ivy |

☆ Learn the words, then use them to do the exercises.

☆ **WORD HUNT**    Which words in the list have these smaller words inside them?

1  din    _____        5  tract  _____

2  ample  _____        6  pan    _____

3  age    _____        7  is     _____

4  mine   _____

☆ **WORD HUNT**    Fill in the gaps with words from the list.

### The Siege

In December, what I had long feared in my (1) _____ now became real.

For days (2) _____ guns were heard in the distance. Then

(3) _____ one week after Christmas Day the siege of our town began. The

date was (4) _____ 1st. Four or five weeks later, (5) _____ 1st

to be (6) _____, the (7) _____ was over. A brief

(8) _____ revealed that all the public buildings, except the

(9) _____ had been destroyed. You can (10) _____ how terrible

I felt in those dreadful times.

☆ **EXPLANATIONS**    Complete these sentences with words from the list.

1  _____ is a kind of creeper.

2  'To put something underground' is to _____ it.

3  If you say 'someone _____ themselves in their books', you mean they

gave all their attention to them.

☆ **WORD MAKER**    Use words from the list to complete the words below.

1  ex _ _ _ _ _ _   (to inspect)          3  ex _ _ _   (to have life)

2  ex _ _ _ _ _   (precisely)           4  ex _ _ _ _ _   (to make larger)

| | | | |
|---|---|---|---|
| loan | preserve | fortunate | compose |
| coax | prepare | unfortunate | advise |
| oath | compare | moderate | promise |
| active | beware | estimate | glimpse |
| action | betray | happiness | sense |

☆ Learn the words, then use them to do the exercises.

☆ **WORD PUZZLE**  Use the word 'fortunate' to help form nine words from the list.

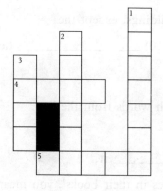

1    f
2    o
3    r
4    t
5    u
6    n
7    a
8    t
9    e

unlucky

to write music

be cautious of

calculate roughly

lucky

joy

liken

be a traitor to

keep whole or safe

☆ **MINI PUZZLE**  Use words from the list to complete the puzzle.

**Clues down**
1 brief view
2 busy
3 to lend

**Clues across**
4 solemn promise
5 awareness

☆ **WORD MATCH**  Find words in the list which mean the same as these words.

1 counsel _____    4 assure _____

2 temperate _____    5 persuade _____

3 deed _____    6 get ready _____

| | | | |
|---|---|---|---|
| wrestle | beggar | produce | chimney |
| wrist | cellar | promote | turkey |
| written | pillar | progress | tune |
| gentleman | grammar | possess | tube |
| heathen | burglar | entire | costume |

☆ Learn the words, then use them to do the exercises.

☆ **WORD HUNT**   Which words in the list have these smaller words inside them?

1  rest  _____

2  is  _____

3  ten  _____

4  men  _____

5  eat  _____

6  him  _____

7  beg  _____

8  ill  _____

9  ram  _____

10  key  _____

11  rod  _____

12  tub  _____

13  tire  _____

14  cost  _____

15  cell  _____

☆ **MINI PUZZLE**   Use words from the list to complete the puzzle.

**Clues down**
1  housebreaker
2  raise to a higher rank
3  own

**Clues across**
4  melody
5  movement forward

☆ **WORD MATCH**   Find words in the list which mean the same as these words.

1  manufacture  _____

2  robber  _____

3  basement  _____

4  grapple  _____

5  whole  _____

6  own  _____

| | | | |
|---|---|---|---|
| discontent | grocer | mention | elbow |
| represent | groceries | attention | growth |
| evident | tempt | situation | speech |
| frequent | attempt | invitation | graze |
| accident | temptation | truly | naked |

☆ Learn the words, then use them to do the exercises.

☆ **WORD PUZZLE** Use words from the list to complete the puzzle.

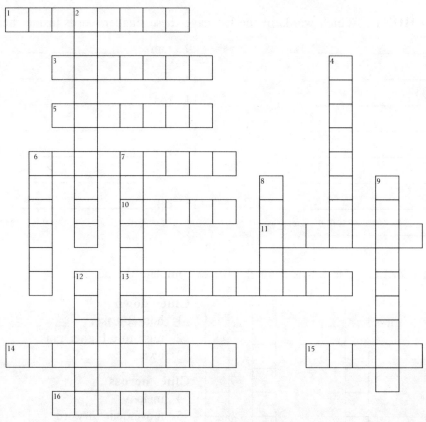

**Clues down**

2 an offer
4 happening very often
6 a talk
7 special care
8 entice
9 provisions
12 a dealer in foodstuffs

**Clues across**

1 unforeseen event
3 obvious
5 try
6 place
10 in truth
11 speak about briefly
13 enticement
14 dissatisfaction
15 without clothes
16 an increase in size

☆ **WORD HUNT** Complete these sentences with words from the list.

1 The cattle are allowed to _____ in the meadow.

2 I hit my _____ on the table and hurt my funny bone.

| accept | honour | labour | sober |
| according | harbour | devour | basin |
| plunge | habit | justice | cabin |
| population | pigeon | practice | rapid |
| satin | gulf | service | payment |

☆ Learn the words, then use them to do the exercises.

☆ **WORD PUZZLE**  Use the word 'population' to help form ten words from the list.

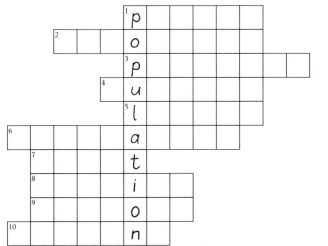

a leap or dive into water

dependent on

repeating an activity to gain skill

fairness

work

all the persons of a country

usual custom

an act of help

a sheltered port

fee

☆ **MINI PUZZLE**  Use words from the list to complete the puzzle.

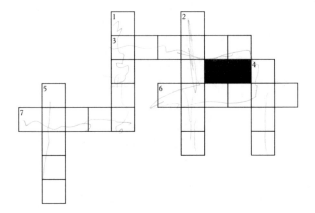

**Clues down**
1 open container for liquids
2 eat
4 large deep bay
5 swift

**Clues across**
3 receive
6 great respect
7 small, simple dwelling hut

☆ **WORD HUNT**  Which words in the list have these smaller words inside them?

1  be _____    3  sat _____

2  pig _____    4  act _____

| | | | |
|---|---|---|---|
| excite | construct | explore | expel |
| exciting | contribute | exploration | angry |
| excellent | consume | explanation | envy |
| exclaim | confirm | style | idea |
| exclaimed | contrast | pavement | oblige |

☆ Learn the words, then use them to do the exercises.

☆ **WORD HUNT** Which words in the list have these smaller words inside them?

1 lent _____          6 sum _____

2 men _____           7 lore _____

3 as _____            8 but _____

4 firm _____          9 plan _____

5 claimed _____       10 rat _____

☆ **WORD HUNT** Complete these sentences with words from the list.

1 The word with the same letters as 'rangy' is _____.

2 The word which means to 'cry out' is _____.

3 The word with the letter 'i' twice is _____.

4 The word which means 'jealousy' is _____.

5 The word with the same letters as 'aide' is _____.

6 The word which means 'build' is _____.

☆ **STEP WORDS** Use words from the list to complete the puzzle.

**Clues down**
2 arouse strong feelings
4 drive out

**Clues across**
1 do a favour to
3 examine closely

| height | junior | gospel | parcel |
| either | language | compel | course |
| neither | monument | chapel | veil |
| reign | department | jewel | vein |
| foreign | swear | bushel | neighbour |

☆ Learn the words, then use them to do the exercises.

☆ **WORD PUZZLE**   Use words from the list to complete the puzzle.

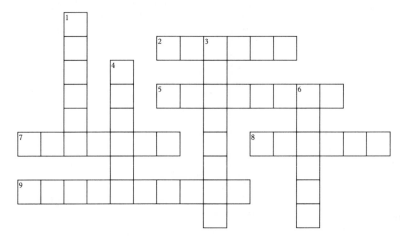

**Clues down**

1   one or the other
3   building to honour
    a great person
4   lower in rank
6   the story of
    Christ's life

**Clues across**

2   force
5   communication
    by speech
7   coming from another
    country
8   eight gallon measure
9   branch of a large
    concern

☆ **WORD MAKER**   Use words from the list to complete the words below.

1   _ ei _      (used to hide face)

2   _ ei _      (vessel to carry blood)

3   _ ei _ _   (period of rule)

4   _ ei _ _ _ _      (not one or other)

5   _ ei _ _ _ _ _ _   (person living next door)

☆ **MINI PUZZLE**   Use the word 'parcel' to help form six words from the list.

| ¹p | | | | wrapped goods |
| ²a | | | take an oath |
| ³r | | | direction |
| ⁴c | | | place of worship |
| ⁵e | | | measure from base to top |
| ⁶l | | | gem |

# Answers

2 WORD PUZZLE **Clues down** (2) nicely
(3) laugh (5) weakness (6) motor (7) lately
(8) laughter (9) victory (10) likely (11) safely
**Clues across** (1) linger (4) likeness (7) laughed
(8) lovely (12) inform (13) lonely (14) visitor
WORD HUNT (1) lonely (2) nicely (3) inform
(4) lately
WORD MAKER (1) lonely (2) likely (3) lovely
(4) lately

3 OPPOSITES (1) distant (2) important
(3) constant (4) admire (5) arrive (6) ashamed
(7) admit
WORD PUZZLE (1) advice (2) amuse
(3) empire (4) though (5) through (6) nature
(7) merchant (8) adventure (9) servant
WORD HUNT (1) servant (2) adventure
(3) amuse (4) distant (5) ashamed (6) adventure
(7) constant

4 WORD HUNT (1) sailor (2) tailor (3) holiday
(4) object (5) equator (6) rough (7) rainy
(8) evening (9) tough (10) enough (11) railway
(12) Rocky (13) daily (14) event (15) robin

5 WORD HUNT (1) carrot (2) village
(3) sparrow (4) scatter (5) cabbage (6) swallow
(7) valleys (8) ragged (9) thought
WORD PUZZLE (1) bought (2) brass
(3) gallop (4) fought (5) village (6) thought
(7) ought
EXPLANATIONS (1) brought (2) scatter
(3) fought (4) valley
WORD HUNT (1) ragged (2) brass (3) gallop

6 WORD PUZZLE **Clues down** (1) against
(2) hasty (4) nasty (5) parish (6) fancy
(9) banish (11) ugly
**Clues across** (1) across (3) alone (7) among
(8) shady (10) study (12) vanish (13) Welsh
(14) polish
WORD MATCH (1) vanish (2) banish
(3) perish (4) hasty (5) ugly (6) among
OPPOSITES (1) hasty (2) against (3) vanish
(4) fancy

7 WORD HUNT (1) famous (2) welcome
(3) lawn (4) dangerous (5) faithfully (6) laid
WORD PUZZLE (1) unable (2) until (3) lays
(4) beauty (5) laying (6) welcome
OPPOSITES (1) dawn (2) beautiful (3) thankful
(4) careful (5) carefully (6) dangerous
WORD MATCH (1) beautiful (2) famous
(3) faithfully

8 WORD MAKER (1) noble (2) kindle
(3) grumble (4) tremble

WORD HUNT (1) protect (2) monster
(3) glance (4) thimble (5) bundle (6) scramble
(7) kindle (8) stumble (9) advance (10) France
(11) grumble (12) distance
WORD PUZZLE **Clues down** (1) stumble
(2) glance (3) advance (4) tremble (6) thimble
(8) bough
**Clues across** (5) monster (7) France (9) noble
(10) plough

9 WORD PUZZLE **Clues down** (1) bucket
(2) tight (3) terror (5) liberty (6) mutton
(7) mighty (10) cotton (12) shrub
**Clues across** (2) trumpet (4) slight (8) error
(9) delight (10) correct (11) Scottish (13) ribbon
(14) blossom
OPPOSITES (1) tight (2) mighty (3) correct
(4) liberty (5) slight
WORD MATCH (1) delight (2) liberty
(3) terror (4) error

10 WORD PUZZLE (1) dislike (2) discuss
(3) discover (4) stalk (5) razor (6) gaze
(7) distinct (8) disgrace
WORD MAKER (1) salt (2) chalk (3) alter
(4) blaze (5) prize (6) size
OPPOSITES (1) lazy (2) discover (3) distress
(4) distinct

11 WORD PUZZLE **Clues down** (1) rubber
(3) bullet (4) station (6) quarrel (7) nation
(8) dictation (9) companion (10) quarter
(13) motion
**Clues across** (2) publish (5) barrel (6) question
(11) quart (12) company (15) astonish
WORD HUNT (1) appear (2) astonish (3) bullet

12 WORD HUNT (1) occupy (2) hollow
(3) combine (4) coffee (5) piece (6) ourselves
WORD PUZZLE **Clues down** (2) occurred
(3) wharf (5) wharves (6) occupy (7) niece
(8) grieve (12) belief
**Clues across** (1) hollow (4) horrid (6) occur
(9) ourselves (10) piece (11) combine
(13) believe (14) forgotten

13 WORD HUNT (1) officer (2) office (3) knit
(4) different (5) skirt (6) bonnet (7) mirror
(8) knitting
WORD MAKER (1) caught (2) taught
(3) daughter (4) naughty (5) stir (6) skirt
(7) mirror
WORD HUNT (1) bonnet (2) stirred (3) skill
(4) different (5) knight

14 WORD PUZZLE **Clues down** (1) foe
(2) steadily (3) butcher (4) statue (7) shilling
(10) tomato (12) poetry (13) weary

Clues across (5) continue (6) potato (8) thread
(9) instead (11) value (14) potatoes (15) wearily
WORD HUNT (1) tomatoes (2) Statue
(3) thread

**15** WORD HUNT (1) tiger (2) cunning
(3) treasure (4) tunnel (5) muddy (6) reward
(7) suppose (8) pleasure (9) pleasant (10) shoe
(11) throat (12) groan (13) defeat (14) coach
(15) measure (16) toast
WORD MATCH (1) cunning (2) pleasure
(3) defeat (4) pleasant

**16** WORD HUNT (1) prettier, prettiest
(2) wedding (3) herring (4) journey (5) dwelling
(6) beginning (7) swept (8) obey, obeyed
(9) group (10) youth
WORD PUZZLE (1) obey (2) vessel (3) group
(4) prettier (5) dwelling (6) wedding (7) prettiest
(8) journey (9) herring
WORD HUNT (1) wound (2) calm (3) crept

**17** STEP WORDS **Clues down** (2) demand
(4) delay
**Clues across** (1) beyond (3) depend
WORD MAKER (1) breath (2) leather
(3) weather (4) feather (5) healthy (6) wealthy
EXPLANATIONS (1) recall (2) shiver
(3) result (4) health (5) meant

**18** WORD PUZZLE **Clues down** (1) queer
(2) steer (4) greedy (5) powder (7) screen
(8) drowned (9) aim (10) petrol
**Clues across** (3) engage (6) praise (8) deer
(11) freedom (12) dairy (13) drown (14) fleet
(15) claim
WORD MATCH (1) screen (2) queer
(3) freedom (4) engage (5) greedy (6) aim

**19** WORD PUZZLE (1) British (2) Irish
(3) season (4) guilty (5) reason (6) crimson
(7) board
WORD HUNT (1) Briton (2) warn (3) Ireland
(4) crimson (5) metal (6) board (7) mental
(8) Briton, iron
WORD MAKER (1) medal (2) mental (3) guide
(4) guest (5) season (6) crimson (7) iron

**20** WORD PUZZLE **Clues down** (1) deserve
(2) rare (3) restore (4) vase (7) refuse (9) retire
(10) October (13) behave
**Clues across** (1) desire (3) relate (5) square
(6) Germany (8) bravery (11) herd
(12) December (14) bathe
WORD HUNT (1) bravery (2) herd (3) retire

**21** WORD PUZZLE **Clues down** (1) wreck
(2) hedge (3) judge (6) check

Clues across (4) attend (5) attack (7) edge
(8) badge
OPPOSITES (1) wrong (2) attack (3) stout
(4) sour
WORD HUNT (1) bridge (2) trout (3) flour
(4) lodge (5) sword

**22** MINI PUZZLE **Clues down** (1) banana
(2) whom (3) score (4) memory
**Clues across** (1) bowl (5) orange (6) wore
(7) factory
WORD MAKER (1) pavement (2) basement
(3) suit (4) fruit
WORD HUNT (1) member (2) remember
(3) weather (4) remembered

**23** WORD PUZZLE **Clues down** (1) huge
(2) truth (3) scripture (5) duty (6) creature
(7) figure
**Clues across** (3) shoulder (4) pour
(5) dumb (6) court (8) using (9) during
WORD HUNT (1) dumb (2) eight (3) weigh
(4) during (5) weight (6) entertain

**24** WORD HUNT (1) piano (2) exchange
(3) drying (4) carrying (5) cities (6) excuse
(7) palace (8) worship
WORD PUZZLE **Clues down** (1) reply
(2) except (5) cities
**Clues across** (2) exchange (3) excuse (4) palace
(6) circle (7) worse
WORD HUNT (1) worst, foggy, city (2) worry

**25** OPPOSITES (1) noisy (2) honest (3) seldom
(4) divide (5) giant (6) wicked (7) earnest
WORD PUZZLE **Clues down** (1) French
(2) mistake
**Clues across** (3) engine (4) selfish
EXPLANATIONS (1) sign (2) search (3) coin
(4) signal (5) Quite

**26** WORD HUNT (1) local (2) people (3) clothes
(4) Wednesday/Tuesday
WORD PUZZLE (1) owe (2) choke (3) idea
(4) fortune (5) area (6) disgust (7) second
(8) family (9) Tuesday
WORD HUNT (1) second, throne (2) several
(3) cruel (4) area (5) disgust (6) family
WORD HUNT (1) fortune (2) area (3) several
(4) throne

**27** WORD PUZZLE **Clues down** (2) navy
(3) clumsy (4) picnic (5) arithmetic (6) collar
(8) farewell (10) flood (13) else
**Clues across** (1) losing (4) pony (7) saucer
(9) aunt (11) holy (12) pencil (14) wooden
(15) ocean
WORD HUNT (1) losing (2) farewell (3) aunt
(4) ocean

**28** WORD PUZZLE **Clues down** (2) lawyer
(3) refer (6) afford (7) account (8) assist
(10) nerve (11) apply
**Clues across** (1) allowed (3) regard (4) drawer
(5) chapter (8) approach (9) clown
(12) address (13) regret
WORD MAKER (1) respect (2) retreat
(3) regret (4) lawyer (5) gardener (6) chapter

**29** WORD PUZZLE **Clues down** (2) confuse
(3) destroyed (4) convict (5) devote (7) describe
(10) sparkle (11) pastime (12) confess (14) vast
**Clues across** (1) detect (4) confine (6) humble
(8) consider (9) vote (10) steeple (13) destroy
(15) ankle (16) feeble
WORD HUNT (1) plaster (2) direct

**30** WORD PUZZLE (1) insist (2) invent
(3) profit (4) dose (5) increase (6) composition
(7) education (8) industry (9) stupid
(10) position (11) inhabit
WORD HUNT (1) whose (2) information
(3) pupil (4) educate (5) credit (6) splendid
(7) insect (8) sole
WORD MATCH (1) peril (2) splendid
(3) profit (4) stupid

**31** OPPOSITES (1) failure (2) future
(3) departure (4) dismay (5) disappear
(6) gradual (7) gradually (8) disorder (9) display
(10) dismiss
EXPLANATIONS (1) manufacture (2) pasture
(3) final (4) equal (5) furniture (6) equally
(7) dismiss (8) really (9) total (10) gradually
(11) usually (12) finally
WORD HUNT (1) dismiss (2) manufacture
(3) disorder (4) display

**32** WORD PUZZLE **Clues down** (1) fully
(2) frozen (3) degree (4) Canada (5) America
(6) Atlantic (9) freeze (12) China (13) sleeve
(14) awful
**Clues across** (5) agreeable (7) yawn (8) breeze
(10) Africa (11) Pacific (13) squeeze (14) Arctic
(15) gem (16) wonderful (17) respectful

**33** WORD PUZZLE (1) decorate (2) entitle
(3) chorus (4) negroes (5) private (6) measles
(7) title (8) climate (9) heroes (10) jungle
MINI PUZZLE **Clues down** (1) echo
(2) pickle (4) negro
**Clues across** (3) cultivate (5) knuckle
(6) single (7) hero
WORD HUNT (1) trample (2) decoration
(3) article (4) climate

**34** WORD PUZZLE **Clues down** (1) sincerely
(4) lantern

**Clues across** (2) protection (3) telephone
(5) sincere (6) sketch (7) condition
WORD HUNT (1) Australia (2) Europe
(3) fraction (4) Asia
WORD HUNT (1) reduction (2) severe
(3) merely (4) switch (5) direction

**35** WORD HUNT (1) shepherd (2) nephew
(3) struggle (4) parrot (5) Southern
(6) Impossible (7) Western (8) Modern
(9) Modest (10) terrible (11) improve
(12) horrible (13) possible (14) puzzle
WORD HUNT (1) limb (2) Northern
(3) saddle

**36** WORD PUZZLE (1) dispute (2) courage
(3) flourish (4) victim (5) disobey (6) district
(7) singular (8) couple (9) displease (10) disturb
WORD HUNT (1) double (2) Regular
(3) popular (4) encourage (5) prey (6) trouble
WORD MAKER (1) popular (2) calendar
(3) regular (4) particular (5) vinegar

**37** WORD PUZZLE **Clues down** (1) rural
(2) mistress (3) canal (5) electric (6) misfortune
(7) election (8) mortal (9) handsome
**Clues across** (4) musical (7) elect (8) mischief
(10) capital (11) royal (12) handkerchief
WORD HUNT (1) halt (2) trial (3) funeral
(4) erect (5) loyal (6) rascal

**38** WORD PUZZLE (1) revive (2) revenge
(3) resemble (4) secret (5) complain (6) bargain
(7) resolve (8) inquire
MINI PUZZLE **Clues down** (1) retain
(2) require (4) torture
**Clues across** (3) feature (5) procure
WORD HUNT (1) request (2) select (3) endure
(4) waist (5) reverse

**39** WORD HUNT (1) ordinary (2) example (3) image
(4) examine (5) extract (6) expand (7) exist, exercise
WORD HUNT (1) imagination (2) enemy
(3) exactly (4) January (5) February (6) exact
(7) exercise (8) examination (9) library
(10) imagine
EXPLANATIONS (1) Ivy (2) bury (3) buried
WORD MAKER (1) examine (2) exactly
(3) exist (4) expand

**40** WORD HUNT (1) unfortunate (2) compose
(3) beware (4) estimate (5) fortunate
(6) happiness (7) compare (8) betray (9) preserve
MINI PUZZLE **Clues down** (1) glimpse
(2) active (3) loan
**Clues across** (4) oath (5) sense
WORD MATCH (1) advise (2) moderate
(3) action (4) promise (5) coax (6) prepare